Shaina of Norway

by **Ella Verzov** • **Chana Oirechman**
Translated by **Yael Mermelstein**

Hi kids! My name's Shaina. I'm nine years old and I live in Oslo, the capital of Norway.

Europe

Asia

rael ⑦

③

②

④

Australia

www.younglamplighters.com | yeladim.e.c@gmail.com

Photography: Israel Bardugo

Layout and Design:
Boaz Sharon - www.keysharon.co.il

Special thanks to Shaina Wilhelm and family
and to her guest Chanshi Lewenthal.

Published by Menucha Publishers Inc.
1235 38th Street, Brooklyn, NY 11218
Tel/Fax: 718-232-0856
1855-Menucha | www.menuchapublishers.com
ISBN: 978161465175-8

"Good morning!"

When I hear my mother's voice I know that it's definitely morning here in Norway. Otherwise, I might get confused. You see, it's summer in Norway now, which means the sun doesn't set for two whole months! That means even if I wake up in the middle of the night, the sun will still be shining. Eight p.m. — the sun is shining! Ten p.m. — still sunny out! Midnight — the sky is still bright blue! At two o'clock in the morning the birds are singing loudly as they welcome in a new day.

Try to imagine this: Shabbat starts around midnight on Friday night, and finishes early Sunday morning!

But in the winter, the sun hides away for most of the day. It rises very late in the morning and sets just a few hours later in the early afternoon. The days feel so short, but they're still long enough to do homework! I can't wait for summer when every day seems like it lasts forever.

The House of Representatives on a Norwegian summer night

Have you ever had a visitor from another country? Today is a very exciting day for me. Today, for the first time in my life, a friend is coming from another country — just to visit me.

I have few Jewish friends my age in Norway. But this summer my mother had a fantastic idea! She suggested that we invite Chanshi, my friend from Denmark, to Norway. Her parents are the Chabad *shluchim* in Copenhagen, the capital of Denmark. Since it's only an hour away from us by plane, we've visited her family several times already. That's how I became friends with her. I bet you have friends that live closer than an hour's plane ride away, but when you're a Chabad *shaliach*, that's considered close.

I'm so excited about my guest!

We arrive at the airport and my mother and I walk excitedly towards the arrivals hall. I have no patience — I just want to see my friend already!

I scan the faces of everyone who walks into the arrivals hall. I see a tall man with a briefcase and a short woman pushing a stroller. I see so many people. But none of them look like Chanshi. And then, suddenly, there she is! My friend Chanshi has arrived!

I run towards her and she runs towards me, lugging a little suitcase behind her.

It's so good to see you, Chanshi!

"*Velkommen til Norge!* Welcome to Norway!" I say. "How was your flight?"

"*Baruch Hashem*, it was good," Chanshi says, smiling shyly.

I smile too. "I'm so happy you came."

We walk towards the exit together. The train is already waiting at the station, as if it was there just to take us home!

On the way to my house, Chanshi looks out the window at the beautiful view. I tell her all about the magical sights of Norway.

Chanshi watches the beautiful landscape

Not far from my house, you can see big cliffs on the horizon with water beneath them. They're called the fjords (pronounced "fyords"). Once, during vacation, we sailed through the gorgeous fjords on a ferry. A ferry is a big boat that transports passengers, cargo, and even cars from place to place. Sailing through the fjords was amazing. Huge cliffs rose up on the right and the left of us. Even though it was summertime, the mountain peaks were still covered with snow. It was spectacular to see.

On the ferry deck

When we get to my house, I show Chanshi my room. I help her unpack her things, and I tell her a little bit about where I live. We speak to each other in English. We each speak four languages. The three languages that we both speak are English, Hebrew, and Yiddish. We could walk down the streets of Norway and speak in a language that nobody else would understand! My fourth language is Norwegian and Chanshi's is Danish. Norwegian and Danish are similar languages.

We look out the window and I point out the tall mountains in the distance. In the winter, those mountains are covered with snow. People practice skiing there at all hours of the day and night. I point out the biggest mountain with the funny-looking slide sticking out of it. It's called Holmenkollen. The slide is actually a world-famous ski jump. Professional skiers come from all over the world to participate in ski-jumping competitions. During the winter, you can watch them practicing their ski jumps on that very mountain! It literally looks like they are flying, just without wings!

Ski jumping

Ski jumping isn't for me, but I'm very good at ice-skating. My parents bought me my own ice skates. During the winter they take me to the park near our house where there's an ice-skating rink. The city pours water all over a field in the park and the water freezes immediately. Voila! We have an enormous ice-skating rink.

Now, in the summer, the mountains are green and flowering, and so is the park near our house. The ice-skating rink is just a grassy field where children play soccer. Soccer doesn't compare to ice-skating, in my opinion!

Ice-skating during the winter

"Come, girls. Lunch is ready," my mother calls to us. We wash our hands and sit down to eat. Of course, the serving dish in the middle of the table is full of sliced salmon.

You can't come to Norway without eating salmon! Salmon is the most popular fish in Norway. The waters of Norway are full of fish, especially high-quality salmon, known throughout the world as Norwegian salmon. The biggest salmon factory in the world is located in Norway. I think Norwegians like salmon as much as Jewish people like gefilte fish!

The port of Oslo is pretty close to my house. The fishermen come to the port with boats stuffed with fish, mostly salmon. Yesterday, in honor of Chanshi's visit, we went to the port and bought a fresh salmon.

At the Oslo port, waiting for the fishing boats

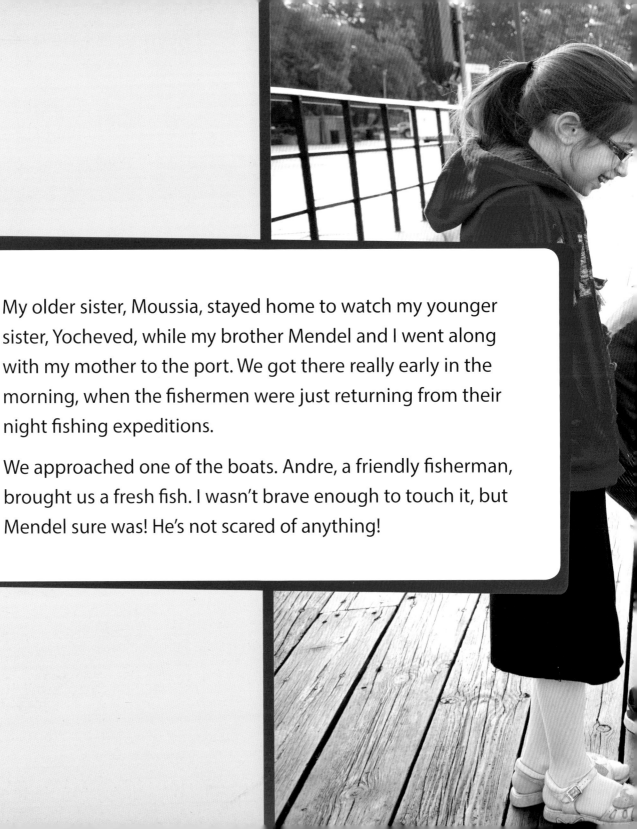

My older sister, Moussia, stayed home to watch my younger sister, Yocheved, while my brother Mendel and I went along with my mother to the port. We got there really early in the morning, when the fishermen were just returning from their night fishing expeditions.

We approached one of the boats. Andre, a friendly fisherman, brought us a fresh fish. I wasn't brave enough to touch it, but Mendel sure was! He's not scared of anything!

Andre the fisherman gives us a fresh fish

Mendel asked to visit Andre's boat. I followed Mendel onto the boat. Andre's boat had many compartments filled with fresh fish that he'd caught just a few hours ago. I didn't want to be rude, but boy did I want to hold my nose!

We put the fish in a bag and Mendel washed his hands to get the fishy smell off of them. Then we hurried home to prepare lunch.

On the fishing boat

At home, we cleaned the fish. While we worked, I started imagining that maybe we'd find a diamond in the belly of the fish. I peeked inside, though, and there was nothing there. Oh well! Maybe next time!

And now the fish is on the table, ready to be eaten. It doesn't say a word about its journey from the sea to our home.

"Enjoy!" my mother says.

"It's delicious. Thank you!" Chanshi says after she tastes Norway's famous fish.

"When we finish eating, I have a surprise for you," I tell her. "I want you to meet some of my special neighbors."

"What's so interesting about your neighbors?" Chanshi asks me.

"You'll see," I say.

Maybe there's a diamond hiding inside?

After we say *Birkat HaMazon*, we hurry outside and cross the street. We pass by a few houses, turn right, and then — we're standing in front of a house that looks very different from all of the other houses in the area. There's a giant plaza with guard booths in front of it.

"Where in the world are we?" Chanshi asked me.

"These are my special neighbors. The king and queen of Norway! This is their palace. Here in Norway it's called *Det Kongelige Slott*, which means 'the royal palace.' Do you want to see it up close?"

Well, who wouldn't want to see a royal palace up close? We get close to the royal guards. In their sleek uniforms they look, well — royal!

A guard at the royal palace

The palace doesn't look like the pictures of palaces that you see in children's books, with spires and fortresses. On the outside, Norway's royal palace looks very big but quite simple. Inside the palace, though, there are beautifully decorated halls, pretty bedrooms, and spacious guest rooms. I wouldn't mind sleeping over at the palace for a night — not that I've ever been invited!

"Most palaces in the world have become museums," I tell Chanshi. "But this palace is not a museum at all. In fact, it's being used right now. Maybe the king and queen of Norway are looking out the window right now and they can see us!"

"We also have a royal palace in Denmark," Chanshi says. "But I've never been inside. Can we go inside this palace?"

"I wish we could," I say. "But the palace is closed to visitors. We can visit the royal gardens around the palace, though. Those are always open to everyone."

Taking a picture at the royal palace

I love the park around the palace. I don't think there are many royal gardens in the world that you can visit any time and you're even allowed to spread a blanket on the floor and make a picnic. We walk past a pretty lake where ducks swim happily. We climb onto one of the bridges to get a closer look. They are so cute.

I ask Chanshi if she knows how to tell the difference between a male and female duck. She doesn't.

"Well," I say, "male ducks usually have colorful feathers and their heads are a shade of metallic green. Female ducks are mostly brown." We climb on to one of the bridges and look down at the ducks, floating on the water and looking for minnows to eat.

On one of the bridges in the park

We walk through rows of beautiful flowers, and then we sit down in the grass and eat some of the snacks that my mother prepared for us. I tell Chanshi all about our lives here in Norway. Even though we live in Oslo, my parents have connections with Jews all over the country. They give Torah classes to Jews of all ages in person, over the phone, and even over Skype. Sometimes my father will travel hours in order to perform a brit milah or to visit a sick person who needs encouragement. Last year I went with my father to run a Chanukah party in a faraway city.

Chanshi tells me about her life in Copenhagen. She tells me about the class she organizes for three-year-old children. Her mother and her older sister help her to prepare the class, and then she teaches it all by herself.

"And I love to bake," Chanshi tells me. "I bake cookies and cake for Shabbat and the *chagim* and to give out at the Torah classes."

"Really? I also love to bake," I say. Now Chanshi and I have another thing in common.

I tell Chanshi about a special activity that I'm a part of — baking for the poor. There's a Jewish lady who lives in Oslo named Janne. Janne owns a boutique where she sells luxury items. At the front of her boutique she opened a small café. All of the money that she makes at the café goes to poor people in Israel. We prepare baked goods at home and bring them to Janne to sell. Any money that Janne earns on our cakes goes straight to the needy. When I bake something for Janne's café, I make sure it's really tasty and that it looks beautiful. That way I hope people will buy it and more money will be given to charity.

"What an original idea!" Chanshi says. "What a great way to give tzedakah. And you get to become an expert baker that way too!"

Baked goods for Janne's café

We finish our tour of the royal gardens and head home. On the way, I get an idea.

As soon as we get home, I ask Chanshi to wait for me in the living room. I run to my room and take my *bunad* out of my closet. The *bunad* is the national dress of Norway. It's very expensive and every Norwegian has only one. I got my *bunad* as a present from a friend who visited us. I've only worn it a handful of times. Today is a great day to wear it again!

"Come see!" I call out to Chanshi.

"Wow! That's interesting," she says. "When do you wear that?"

"On very special occasions! Like when my friend Chanshi Lewenthal visits from Denmark," I say. We both laugh so hard.

Putting on my bunad for Chanshi

"Shaina and Chanshi, it's almost five o' clock," my mother calls from the living room. "It's time to go and visit Lee."

Chanshi goes to the living room, and I go and change back into my regular clothing.

Lee lives quite near my house. She's my best friend in Norway. We like to get together on Shabbat, holidays, and sometimes after school. I love it most when we have sleepovers together.

A while ago, I explained to Lee how important it is to have a mezuzah on the door in order to protect us and our homes. Lee really wanted a mezuzah for her room. She asked her parents, and they agreed! They asked my father to come and help them to put it up.

"My father is going to help Lee's family with the mitzvah of mezuzah today," I tell Chanshi. "Lee wants me to come along and of course you're coming too! You're my guest and I'm sure that Lee will be very excited to meet you."

With my good friend Lee

Here we are at Lee's house. We knock on the door and her mother answers.

"Rabbi Wilhelm and the girls are here!" Lee's mother calls out happily. Lee and her younger sister run to the door.

Lee is excited to meet Chanshi. I've already told them about each other, but this is the first time they're meeting in person. I'm surrounded by close friends. I feel rich with friendship!

In the meantime, we all go to Lee's room. My father places the mezuzah on the right doorpost and makes a *berachah*: "*Baruch atah Hashem Elokeinu melech ha'olam asher kideshanu b'mitzvotav v'tzivanu likvoa mezuzah.*"

Lee is glowing as she reaches out to kiss her very own mezuzah for the first time. She knows how important this mitzvah is.

It's time to go. Chanshi and I say good-bye to Lee.

Now Lee has a mezuzah too!

After we leave her house, I tell Chanshi, "I have another surprise for you. We're going to the forest!"

There are many forests in Norway. They aren't the scary kind of forests that you read about. There's one right near my house. The forests in Norway are full of berries and many different kinds of mushrooms at this time of the year. I love picking through the bushes for berries and filling baskets with mushrooms. I know that Chanshi has forests in Denmark too, but she doesn't have me there to pick mushrooms with her!

We take a few straw baskets and soon enough we're walking through the forest, looking for mushrooms and berries. Mushrooms grow in clusters, underneath the trees. Our voices echo through the forest as we call out, "I found some!" and "Over here! There are a lot here!" Half an hour later, our baskets are full of fresh mushrooms and sweet berries.

It's fun to pick mushrooms together

We follow the path out of the forest, and there we find a mushroom-checking station in front of us. What's a mushroom-checking station? That's where volunteers who are mushroom experts sit and wait for people like us. I'll bet you never met a mushroom-checking expert before! These experts know which mushrooms are safe to eat and which ones are poisonous.

An older man sits at his checking station, a pile of logs with a wooden plank on top of it. He pours our mushrooms out onto the wooden surface. Then he throws out all of the mushrooms we can't eat and gives us back our basket with all of the mushrooms that are safe to eat.

"*Takk* (thank you)," we tell him.

"*Var sho goo* (you're welcome)," he answers.

But our volunteer checker doesn't know how to check for everything! When we get home, my mother will check that the mushrooms and berries do not have any bugs, and then they will be kosher for us to eat!

Here are the mushrooms that are safe to eat

We come home tired but happy.

"It's getting late, girls," my mother tells us. "Time to go to sleep."

I can't even say, "But I don't want to go to sleep! It's still light outside." It's always light out in Norway during the summer!

Chanshi and I wash up and get ready to go to sleep.

"We did so much today," I hear Chanshi say from her bed. "But I'm still sad that the day is over."

"The day may be over," I say, "but the sun continues to shine."

I can't help thinking that we're here to add light in Norway too. I feel so lucky to be a Rebbe's *shaliach* in Norway. We are able to bring the light and warmth of Torah and mitzvot to the Jews of Norway — not just in the summer — but all year long.

Bringing the taste of Shabbat to the Jews of Oslo

Now how do you like that?

Fascinating Facts about Norway

Scandinavia is a region in Northern Europe. It is a peninsula (that's almost an island, but only three sides are surrounded by water) containing three countries: Norway, Sweden, and Denmark.

Norway is bordered by Sweden in the east, Finland and Russia in the northeast, the Arctic Ocean in the north, the Norwegian Sea in the west, and the North Sea in the north.

The name *Norway* means "The Northern Path."

Norway is full of fjords. A fjord is a narrow body of water connected to the sea that runs deep in a valley between two steep walls. A fjord is formed mostly from ice glaciers that "meet" warmer waters and melt. Fjords are freshwater lakes (not salty!).

The Norwegian winter is cold, long, and dark. There are months where the sun only shines a few hours a day. In more northerly cities the sun doesn't rise or set at all for approximately four months — there is only darkness.

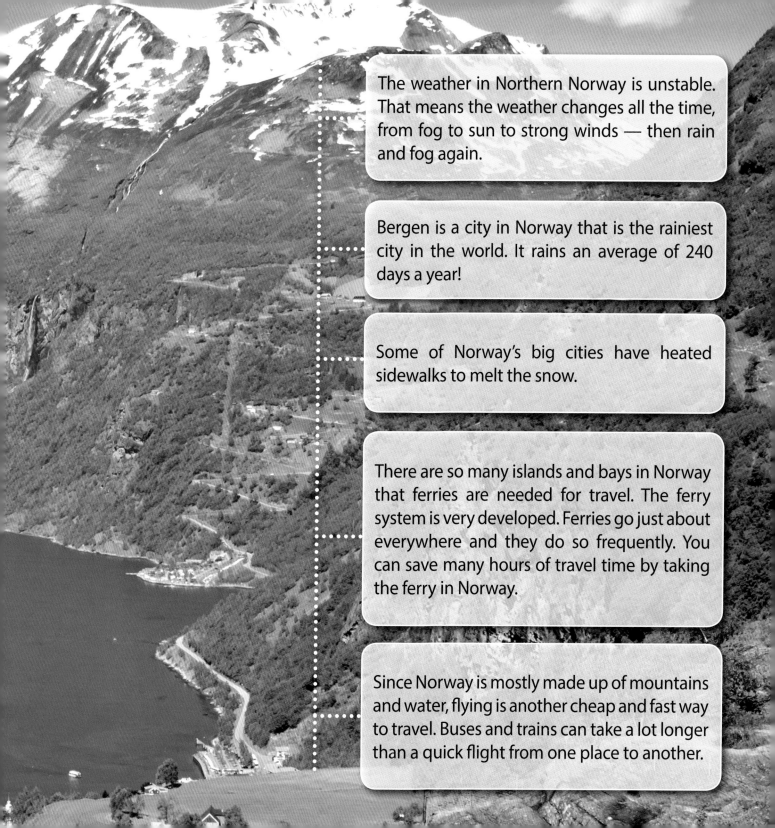

The weather in Northern Norway is unstable. That means the weather changes all the time, from fog to sun to strong winds — then rain and fog again.

Bergen is a city in Norway that is the rainiest city in the world. It rains an average of 240 days a year!

Some of Norway's big cities have heated sidewalks to melt the snow.

There are so many islands and bays in Norway that ferries are needed for travel. The ferry system is very developed. Ferries go just about everywhere and they do so frequently. You can save many hours of travel time by taking the ferry in Norway.

Since Norway is mostly made up of mountains and water, flying is another cheap and fast way to travel. Buses and trains can take a lot longer than a quick flight from one place to another.

In Northern Norway you can see one of the most amazing wonders of creation: The northern lights, also known as the aurora borealis. It is a spectacular light show in the night sky. Colorful waves of light flicker quickly in the sky for minutes, hours, or even days. The most common color of the northern lights is green, but sometimes you can also see blue, yellow, red, white, and purple.

Norway is a kingdom with a king and a queen. They represent Norway to the rest of the world. They officiate at important ceremonial and formal events. All the laws and decisions as to how Norway is run, however, are left up to the elected government.

The longest tunnel road in the world can be found in Norway. It is fifteen miles long, and it takes twenty minutes to drive through it.

The longest wooden staircase in the world can be found in Norway. It is built from 4,444 wooden steps and is nearly a mile long.

Until the nineteenth century, Jews were not allowed to live in Norway. Today 1,800 Jews live there, most of them in the capital, Oslo.

In the beginning of the twentieth century, a beautiful shul was built in Oslo. The shul wasn't damaged during the Holocaust because the Nazis used it to store their books and Jewish property they'd confiscated. Even the Torah scrolls survived the war in one piece.

The governments of Denmark and Sweden saved their Jewish citizens during the Holocaust. Unfortunately, the third Scandinavian country, Norway, cooperated with the Nazis. Almost half of Norway's Jewish population died during the Holocaust. The rest of the Jews escaped to nearby Sweden with the help of the Norwegian underground — a band of resistance fighters from Norway who were against the Nazis. In 2013 (5773), seventy years after the Holocaust, the government of Norway apologized for the way they behaved during that time.

The northernmost Jewish community in the world is in Trondheim, in Northern Norway.

The geographical location of Norway creates many interesting questions in Jewish law. There are places where the sun never sets during the summer and it never rises during the winter. If you visit Norway in the winter, you'd need to ask a rabbi when to say Shema, when to put on tefillin, and when to light Shabbat candles.

In 2004 (5764), a Chabad House was opened in a central location, close to the royal palace in Oslo. The Chabad House serves all Jews living in Norway.

Berry Jam

Ingredients:

- 2 pounds of berries
- 3 cups sugar
- 2–3 tablespoons vanilla extract
- ¼ cup red wine
- peel of 1 lemon, grated
- 1–2 tablespoons freshly squeezed lemon juice

- a pot with a thick bottom
- a wooden spoon
- a glass jar

Directions:

Wash and check the berries and put them in the pot.

Cook the berries on a low flame for a few minutes, mixing occasionally.

When the berries start to give off liquid, crush them gently with your wooden spoon. You don't need to crush all of them.

Now it's time to add the wine, vanilla, and lemon peel. Mix everything together and cook for an additional two minutes.

Add the sugar. Continue cooking and stirring for about ten minutes, until the liquid becomes less. Remove the foam that was created during the cooking.

The jam in the pot is still hot, so it doesn't look thick. When it cools, it will be the thickness you want. It's better to stop cooking the jam too early than to overcook it.

As soon as you turn off the flame, add lemon juice until you like the taste.

Mix, cool, and store in a jar in your fridge.

Enjoy!

The Forests of Norway Are Berry Nice!

About one-quarter of Norway is covered in forests. During the summer months, berries grow all over the forests: mulberries, raspberries, currants, cranberries, blueberries, and others. Berry is the general name given to fruit that comes from flowering plants. Most berries are small, sweet, and tangy, with bold colors: red, black, or purple.

Berries grow in counties with relatively cold climates: Russia, the United States, Canada, and many European countries. They ripen and are ready to be picked during the summer months. They can be eaten or used for decoration. Yum!

Say it in Norwegian!

Hello — Hallo

How are you — Hvordan har du det

Please — Var so snill

Thank you — Takk

Mommy — Mama

Daddy — Papa

Boy — Gutt

Girl — Jente

Friend (m) — Venn

Friend (f) — Venninne

Game — Leketoy

Book — Bok

Car — Bil

Other books in the **Young Lamplighters** series

Tamar of Venice: Seven-year-old Tamar lives in a special city built entirely on water. She travels to school in a boat and there are only two students in her class. Come travel with Tamar, the young lamplighter in Venice, a city of canals and bridges.

1

Moshe of Japan: Eight-year-old Moshe was born in Japan. He studies in a virtual classroom with students from all over the world. His best friend lives in China, a five-hour plane ride away. Come travel with Moshe, the young lamplighter in the city of Tokyo, the capital of Japan.

2

Mendy of Siberia: Five-year-old Mendy lives in Siberia. The Siberian winter lasts more than half the year. Mendy loves sledding on the snow, touring a city built entirely of ice, and helping his parents to prepare for the Chanukah holiday. Come travel with Mendy, the young lamplighter in the city of Krasnoyarsk, in frozen Siberia.

3

Rivka of Thailand: Eight-year-old Rivka lives in Bangkok, the capital of Thailand. Rivka enjoys visiting the floating market, drinking coconut milk straight from the shell, and watching Lampung the chef dice vegetables into a huge frying pan. Come travel with Rivka, the young lamplighter in the Far East, in the tropical country of Thailand.

4

Explore the world with the Young Lamplighters